Little Fish Books about You and Me

British Commonwealth Edition
Published by Scripture Union
London, England.

North American Edition Including Canada
Published by Regal Books
A Division of Gospel Light
Ventura, California, USA

© Gordon Stowell 1984

First Edition 1984. Reprinted 1987, 88, 91, 92, 93.

Co-edition arranged with the help of
Angus Hudson, London

Printed and Bound in Great Britain by
BPCC Hazell Books Ltd, Paulton

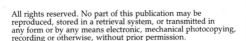

Little Fish Books about You and Me

God
loves

illustrated by Gordon Stowell

God loves me.

He cares for me all the time.

God loves grown-ups.

We love Him too.

God loves baby.

He is making him
big and strong.

God loves Granny
and Grandpa.

I love to see them.

God loves my friends.

God loves my uncles
and aunts.

God loves the shopkeeper.

God loves the postman.

God loves the truck driver.

God loves the train driver.

God loves all the animals.

He loves all the birds.

God loves all of us.

Thank You God!

It's fun

Little Fish Books about You and Me

Please God

Little Fish Books about You and Me

God knows

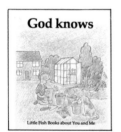

Little Fish Books about You and Me

Thank You God

Little Fish Books about You and Me

 Little Fish Books

I'm Sorry

Little Fish Books about You and Me

God loves

Little Fish Books about You and Me

Help me God

Little Fish Books about You and Me

I Like

Little Fish Books about You and Me

bout You and Me